# SONG OF IRELAND

PUBLISHED BY
WISE PUBLICATIONS
NEW YORK/LONDON/SYDNEY

EXCLUSIVE DISTRIBUTORS:
MUSIC SALES LIMITED,
LONDON,
ENGLAND.

COVER DESIGN DAVID HILLMAN
ILLUSTRATION PETER DENMARK

# CONTENTS

# WHEN IRISH EYES ARE SMILING

Words by
CHAUNCEY OLCOTT &
GEO. GRAFF JNR.

Music by
ERNEST R. BALL

CHORUS.

When Ir_ish eyes are smiling, Sure it's like a morn in Spring___ In the

lilt of Ir_ish laughter, You can hear the an_gels sing___ When Ir_ish

hearts are happy___ All the world seems bright and gay,___ And when Ir_ish eyes are

smil___ing, Sure they steal your heart a_way. When _way.___

# SPINNING WHEEL (THE)

## ( IRISH BALLAD )

Words & Music by
JOHN FRANCIS WALLER &
DELIA MURPHY

**CHORUS**

Mer - ri -ly, cheer - i -ly, nois - i - ly whirr - ing Swings the wheel, spins the wheel
Slow - er, and slow - er, and slow - er the wheel swings, Low - er, and low - er, and

while the foot's stirr - ing Spright - ly and light - ly and air - i - ly ring - ing
low - er the reel rings; Ere the reel and the wheel stopp'd their spin - ning and mov - ing,

Sounds the sweet voice of the young maid - en sing - ing.
Thro' the grove the young lov - ers by moon - light are rov - ing.

# THE SPINNING WHEEL

1. Mellow the moonlight to shine is beginning,
   Close by the window young Eileen is spinning;
   Bent o'er the fire her blind grandmother, sitting,
   Is crooning and moaning and drowsily knitting.

   *Chorus*
   Merrily, cheerily, noisily, whirring,
   Swings the wheel, spins the wheel, while the foot's stirring,
   Sprightly and lightly and airily ringing
   Sounds the sweet voice of the young maiden singing.

2. "Eileen, a chara,† I hear someone tapping,"
   "'Tis the ivy, dear mother, against the glass flapping,"
   "Eily, I surely hear somebody sighing,"
   "'Tis the sound, mother dear, of the autumn winds dying."
   *Chorus*

3. "What's that noise that I hear at the window I wonder?"
   "'Tis the little birds chirping the holly-bush under"
   "What makes you be pushing and moving your stool on?"
   "And singing all wrong that old song of Coolin?"
   *Chorus*

4. There's a form at the casement, the form of her true love,
   And he whispers with face bent, "I'm waiting for you, love"
   "Get up on the stool, through the lattice step lightly,
   And we'll rove in the grove while the moon's shining brightly."
   *Chorus*

5. The maid shakes her head, on her lips lays her fingers,
   Steals up from the seat, longs to go and yet lingers;
   A frightened glance turns to her drowsy grandmother,
   Puts one foot on the stool, spins the wheel with the other.
   *Chorus*

6. Lazily, easily, swings now the wheel round,
   Slowly and lowly is heard now the reel's sound;
   Noiseless and light to the lattice above her
   The maid steps, then leaps to the arms of her lover.

   *Chorus*
   Slower, and slower, and slower the wheel swings,
   Lower, and lower, and lower the reel rings;
   Ere the reel and the wheel stopped their spinning and moving,
   Through the grove the young lovers by moonlight are roving.

† *Pronounced "Kaura"*

# PATSY FAGAN

## ( THE DACENT IRISH BOY )

Words & Music by
THOMAS P. KEENAN

Printed by permission of Waltons (Publications Dept.) Ltd., North Frederick Street, Dublin, Eire.

CHORUS

"Hel - lo Pat-sy Fa-gan!"You can hear the girls all cry "Hel - lo Pat-sy Fa-gan, you're the ap-ple of me eye. You're a da-cent boy from Ire-land, there's no one can de--ny, You're a ra-rem ta-rem div-il-may ca-rem da-cent I-rish boy. Now boy.__

*rall last time*

**2**

Now if there's one among you,
   Would like to marry me,
I'll take her to a little home
   Across the Irish Sea.
I'll dress her up in Satin,
   And please her all I can,
And let her people see thāt I'm
   A dacent Irishman.

**3**

The day that I left Ireland,
   'Twas many years ago.
I left me home in Antrim
   Where the pigs and praties grow.
But since I left auld Ireland,
   It's always been my plan
To let the people see that I'm
   A dacent Irishman.

# IF YOU'RE IRISH COME INTO THE PARLOUR

Words & Music by
SHAUN GLENVILLE &
FRANK MILLER

Moderato.

In sweet Lim-rick Town, they say,.................... Lived a chap named
Patrick loved the girl he wed,.................... But he could not

Patrick John Mol-loy,.................... Once he sail'd to U. S. A.,.................... His luck in for-eign
stand his Ma-in-law,.................... Once with joy he turned quite red,.................... When she got in-to

parts he thought he'd try.................... Now he's made his name, and is a wealthy man,.... He
trou-ble thro' her jaw.................... Six Po-lice they had..... to take her to the court,.... She

put a bit a-way for a rain-y day;.................... So if you gaze up-on........ The
was in-formed a month she would have to do,.................... So Patrick quick-ly wrote Up

# MOUNTAINS O' MOURNE (THE)

Words & Music by
PERCY FRENCH &
HOUSTON COLLISSON

**Andante**

*p*

G    B7    C6#4 / C    C#°    G    D7 G9 G Cm6 G / Add4

1 Oh! Ma - ry! this Lon-don's a won - der-ful sight, Wid the peo-ple here
2 I be-lieve that, when writ-in', a wish you ex - press'd, As to how the fine

G    D13 D7 / Add4    Em    Em    C    D9 D7

work-in' by day and by night; They don't sow pot - a - tes, nor bar - ley, nor
la - dies in Lon-don were dress'd. Well, if you'll be - lieve me, when axed to a

G C G    D13 D7 D#°    Em Em / Add4

wheat, But there's gangs o' them dig - gin' for gold in the street; At
ball, Faith they don't wear a top to their dress - es at all. Oh, I've

A7    C9 D7    C9 D7    G Am7 G

# ISLE OF INNISFREE (THE)

Words & Music by
RICHARD FARRELLY

# GALWAY BAY

Words & Music by
DR. ARTHUR COLAHAN

Published by permission of Pigott & Co. Ltd., 112 Grafton Street, Dublin.

# DELANEY'S DONKEY

Words & Music by
WILLIAM HARGREAVES

Moderato

1 De - la - ney had a don - key ev - 'ry - one ad - mired; Tem - po - 'ri - ly la - zy,
2 The mus - cles of the migh - ty, nev - er known to flinch, Did - n't move the don - key
3 The crowd be - gan to cheer it. Raf - fer - ty, the judge, Came up to as - sist them,

per - ma - nent - ly tired; A leg at ev - 'ry corn - er bal - anc - ing its head, And a
quar - ter of an inch. De - la - ney lay ex - haust - ed, hang - ing round its throat With a
still it would - n't budge. The jock - ey who was rid - ing, lit - tle John Mac - Gee, Was so

tail to let you know which end it want - ed to be fed. Ri - ley sly - ly
grip just like a Scotch - man on a twen - ty - shill - ing note. Start - er, Cart - er,
thor - ough - ly dis - gust - ed he went home to get his tea. Ha - gan, Fa - gan,

said, "We've un-der-rat-ed it. Why not train it?" then he took a rag, Rubbed it, scrubbed it,
lined up all the rest of 'em; When it saw them, it was will-ing then. Raced up, braced up,
stu - dents of psy-chol-o-gy, Swore they'd shift it with some dyn-a-mite; Bought it, brought it,

E7    Am    Adim    E7    Am    C    F

oiled and em-bro-cat-ed it, Got it to the post, and when the start - er dropped the flag,
read - y for the best of 'em; They start-ed off to cheer it but it changed its mind a - gain.
then with out a-pol-o-gy The don-key gave a sneeze and blew the darn stuff out of sight.

G    G7    C    F    C    G

**REFRAIN**

There was Ri - ley push - ing it, shov - ing it, and shush - ing it,
There was Ri - ley push - ing it, shov - ing it, and shush - ing it,
There was Ri - ley push - ing it, shov - ing it, and shush - ing it,

G7    C    F

Ho - gan, Lo - gan, ev - 'ry-one in town, Lined up at-tack-ing it,
Ho - gan, Lo - gan, Ma - ry Ann Mac-graw, She start - ed pok-ing it,
Ho - gan, Lo - gan, all the bal-ly crew, P'lice, and aux-il - 'ar - y, the

C    Cdim    C    G7    C

# LITTLE BIT OF HEAVEN (A)

## ( SHURE THEY CALL IT IRELAND )

Words by
J. KEIRN BRENNAN

Music by
ERNEST R. BALL

Sub-published by B. Feldman & Co. Ltd., 138-140 Charing Cross Road, London WC2H 0LD
for the British Commonwealth of Nations (excluding Canada & Australasia) & the Republic of Ireland.

30

# DID YOUR MOTHER COME FROM IRELAND?

Words & Music by
JIMMY KENNEDY &
MICHAEL CARR

# HOW CAN YOU BUY KILLARNEY?

Words & Music by
HAMILTON KENNEDY, FREDDIE GRUNDLAND,
GERALD MORRISON & TED STEELS

REFRAIN

# GARDEN WHERE THE PRATIES GROW (THE)

Words & Music by
JOHNNY PATTERSON

Arr. by
SAMUEL LIDDLE

# IT'S A GREAT DAY FOR THE IRISH

Words & Music by
ROGER EDENS

CHORUS

# MACUSHLA

Words by
JOSEPHINE ROWE

Music by
DERMOT MacMURROUGH

# THAT'S AN IRISH LULLABY

Words & Music by
J.R. SHANNON

# SWEET ROSIE O'GRADY

Words and Music by
MAUDE NUGENT

Tempo di Valse

Moderato

With-in a charm-ing cot-tage near the place that saw my birth, There
I nev-er shall for-get the day she prom-ised to be mine, As

dwells the sweet-est lit-tle flow'r that ev-er grew on earth. This flow'r is known as Ros-ie, 'tis her
we sat tell-ing love tales with a hap-pi-ness di-vine. Up-on her fin-ger then I placed a

love-ly chris-tian name, But had she an-y oth-er name, I'd love her just the same.
small en-gage-ment ring, While in the trees the lit-tle birds this love song seem'd to sing.

REFRAIN

# PADDY McGINTY'S GOAT

Words & Music by
R.P. WESTON, BERT LEE
AND THE TWO BOBS

# WILD COLONIAL BOY (THE)

Words & Music by
JOSEPH M. CROFTS

Moderato

on - ly son And his mo - ther's pride and joy,___ And dear - ly did his
poach - in' trout, He was the rale "Mc - Coy,"___ And all the neigh - bours

Eb    Fm7    F9    F7    Bb7    Eb

1.2.3.4.    Fine

pa - rents love, The Wild Co - lo - nial Boy    At Boy___
loved young Jack, The Wild Co - lo - nial

Ab    Fm    Bb7    Eb    Gdim    Bb7    Eb    molto rall    f

3. At the early age of sixteen years
   He left his native home.
   And to Australia's sunny land
   He was inclined to roam.
   He robbed the rich, and he helped the poor,
   He stabbed James MacEvoy.
   A terror to Australia was
   The Wild Colonial Boy.

4. For two more years this daring youth
   Ran on his wild career.
   With a head that knew no danger
   And a heart that knew no fear.
   He robbed outright the wealthy squires,
   And their Arms he did destroy;
   And woe to all who dared to fight
   The Wild Colonial Boy.

5. He loved the Prairie and the Bush,
   Where Rangers rode along:
   With his gun stuck in it's holster deep,
   He sang a merry song.
   But if a foe once crossed his track,
   And sought him to destroy,
   He'd get sharp shootin' sure from Jack,
   The Wild Colonial Boy.

6. One morning on the prairie wild,
   Jack Duggan rode along,
   While listening to the mocking bird
   Singing a cheerful song.
   Out jumped three troopers, fierce and grim,
   Kelly, Davis and Fitzroy:
   They all set out to capture him,
   The Wild Colonial Boy.

7. "Surrender now, Jack Duggan, Come!
   You see there's three to one!
   Surrender in the Queen's name, Sir!
   You, are a plundering Son!"
   Jack drew two pistols from his side,
   And glared upon Fitzroy:
   "I'll fight, but not surrender!" cried
   The Wild Colonial Boy.

8. He fired a shot at Kelly
   Which brought him to the ground
   He fired point blank at Davis, too
   Who fell dead at the sound.
   But a bullet pierced his brave young heart
   From the pistol of Fitzroy:
   And that was how they captured him,
   The Wild Colonial Boy.

# MICK McGILLIGAN'S BALL

Words & Music by
MICHAEL CASEY

ev - 'ry - one For to have some mu - sic and some rare old fun.
two old Skins Came a - long at a gal - lop with two Miss Quinns.
do de - clare, Ask that grand old Hool - ey down in sweet Kil - dare.

CHORUS

So they
And they } All went down to Mick Mc Gill - i - gan's Ba - - - - - ll Where they had to tear the pa - per of the
When they }

wa - - - - ll, To make room for all the peo - ple in the ha - - - ll, Oh, the girls and the boys made a

dev - il of a noise At Mick Mc - Gill - i - gan's Ball. So they Ball. B. A. dou - ble L Ball.

# PHIL THE FLUTER

Words & Music by
PERCY FRENCH &
DAVID HENEKER

how he'd like their com-pan-y that eve-ning at the ball. And when writ-in' out he was
on - ly make the pi - per play 'The hare is in the corn'" So Phil plays up to the
got to pay the pi - per when he tooth-ers on the flute" Then all joined in wid the

*E7* *Am* *C* *F* *G7* *C* *E7*

care - ful to sug-gest to them, That if they found a hat of his con -
best of his a - bil - i - ty, The la - dy and the gen - tle - man be -
great - est jo - vi - al - i - ty, ___ Cov - er - ing the Buc - kle and the

*Am* *C* *E7*

-ven-ient to the door The more they put in, when - ev - er he re-quest-ed them The
-gin to do their share; While young Mick was a' pran-cing with a - gil - i - ty De-
Shuf - fle and the Trent Jigs were danced, of the ve - ry fin - est qual - i - ty, The

*Am* *D7* *G7* *C* *E7* *Am* *C*

bet - ter would the mu - sic be for bat - ter-ing the floor. With the
-crep - it Mrs___ Caf - fer - ty was lep - pin' like a hare. With the
wid - ow found a hus - band and the flu - ter found the rent. With the

*G7*

CHORUS

# PEGGY O'NEIL

Words & Music by
HARRY PEASE, ED. G. NELSON
& GILBERT DODGE

1. Peg-gy O'-Neil is a girl who could steal An-y heart, an-y-where, an-y time,___ And
2. Ev-'ry-thing's plann'd for a wed-ding so grand, In the spring I will bring her the ring,___ Then

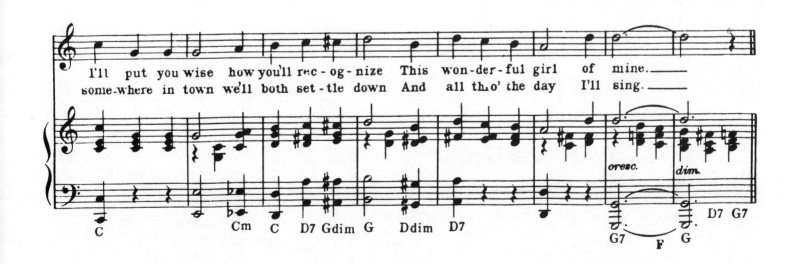

I'll put you wise how you'll rec-og-nize This won-der-ful girl of mine.___
some-where in town we'll both set-tle down And all tho' the day I'll sing.___

**CHORUS**

# EILEEN ALANNAH

Words by
E.S. MARBLE

Music by
J.R. THOMAS

# LET HIM GO, LET HIM TARRY

Irish Song
Arranged by
EVERETT LYNTON

1. Fare-well to cold win - ter, sum-mer's come at last.
2. He wrote me a let - ter say-ing he was ve - ry bad. I
3. Some of his friends had a good kind wish for me
4. He can go to his old mo-ther now and set her mind at ease, I

No-thing have I gained but my true love I have lost. I'll sing and I'll be hap-py like the
sent him back an an-swer say-ing I was aw-ful glad. He wrote to me an-oth-er say-ing
Oth-ers of his friends they could hang me on a tree. But soon I'll let them see my love, and
hear she is an old, old wo-man, ve-ry hard to please. It's slight-ing me and talk-ing ill is

birds up-on the tree, For since_ he de-ceived me_ I care no more for he.
he was well and strong, But I care no more a-bout him than the ground he walks up-on.
soon I'll let them know That I can get a new sweetheart on an-y grounds I go.
what she's al-ways done Be-cause that I was court-ing_ her great big ug-ly son.

Eb6/Bb   Cm6/Bb   Bb        F7                    Eb/F  F7  Bb

## CHORUS

Let him go, let him tar-ry, let him sink or let him swim.

Bb   Bbmaj7   Bb6      Bb        Eb6/   Cm6/      Bb
                                 Bb     Bb

He does-n't care for me nor I don't care for him. He can go and get an-oth-er that I

F7                          Eb/F  F7  Bb   F13   Bb   Bbmaj7   Bb7

1

hope he will en-joy, For I'm going to mar-ry a far nic-er boy. Let him

Eb6/Bb  Cm6/Bb  Bb   F7                                      Bb

2              D.S. %  Last time.

far nic-er boy.   far nic-er boy.

F7  Eb/F  F7  Bb    F7  Eb/F  F7  Bb.    F7              Eb6  F7  Bb

# ROSE OF TRALEE (THE)

Words by
E. SPENCER
Music by
C. GLOVER

Arr. by
H. NICHOLLS

**Slowly** (*with feeling*)

The pale moon was ris-ing a-bove the green moun-tain, The
The cool shades of ev'-ning their man-tle were spread-ing, And

sun was de-clin-ing be-neath the blue sea, When I stray'd with my
Ma-ry all smil-ing was list-'ning to me, The moon through the

love to the pure crys-tal foun-tain That stands in the beau-ti-ful
val-ley her pale rays was shed-ding, When I won the heart of the

# TROTTING TO THE FAIR

Words by
ALFRED PERCEVAL GRAVES

Music arranged by
CHARLES VILLIERS STANFORD

# DANNY BOY

## ( EILY DEAR )

Words by
FRED E. WEATHERLEY

# O'RAFFERTY'S MOTOR CAR

Words & Music by
TOMMIE CONNOR

gal - lon of stout in the pet - rol tank, it does nine - ty miles an hour.____
chas - sis came off of a tink - er's cart that col - lapsed in Phoe - nix Park!
mo - ment that Din - ny treads on the break, then his foot goes thro' the floor.____ Oh
reck - on he'd on - ly get half a quid if he took it to the pawn.____
-way on top of the G. P. O. with his L plates round his neck.____

**CHORUS**

what a won - der - ful mo - tor car, it's the great - est ev - er seen____ It used to be black as me

fath - er's hat, now it's for - ty shades of green____ On tee vee and the ra - di - o and in

ev - 'ry pub - lic bar,____ The burn - ing ques - tion of the day, is O' Raf - fer - ty's mo - tor

1, 2, 3, 4

car____

2. Now
3. Now
4. Now
5. Now car____

# I KNOW WHERE I'M GOING

Arr. by HERBERT HUGHES

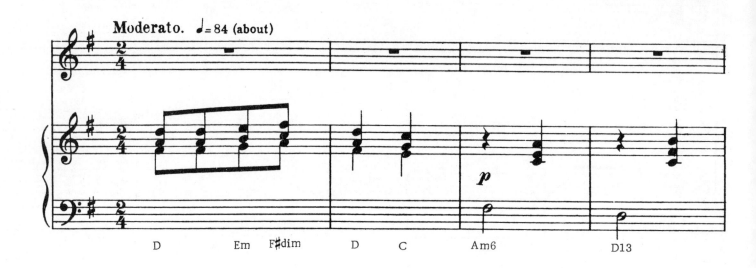

Moderato. ♩ = 84 (about)

D    Em    F♯dim    D    C    Am6    D13

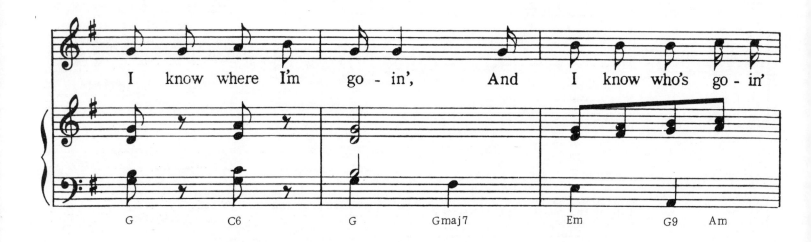

I know where I'm go - in', And I know who's go - in'

G    C6    G    Gmaj7    Em    G9    Am

with me, I know who I love, But the

G    D7    G    Em

*Black: dour, ungracious.

# MOTHER MACHREE

Words by
RIDA JOHNSON YOUNG

Music by
CHAUNCEY OLCOTT &
ERNEST R. BALL